PINKFONG: BABY SHARK AND THE COLOURFUL BALLOONS.
A CENTUM BOOK 978-1-912841-63-9
Published in Great Britain by Centum Books Ltd.
This edition published 2018.
1 3 5 7 9 10 8 6 4 2

Original Korean edition first published by Smart Study Co., Ltd.

This edition published by Centum Books Ltd in 2018 by arrangement with Smart Study Co., Ltd.

Centum Books Ltd, 20 Devon Square, Newton Abbot, Devon, TQ12 2HR, UK.

books@centumbooksltd.co.uk

CENTUM BOOKS Limited Reg. No. 07641486.

A CIP catalogue record for this book is available from the British Library.

Printed in Poland.

Baby Shark Family & Friends

Baby Shark

Baby Shark lives under the ocean and is curious about everything around him. He likes to sing. When he's scared, he sings to help him feel brave.

Mummy Shark

There are no limits to the things that Mummy Shark can do! She always listens to Baby Shark and they share a very special bond.

Daddy Shark

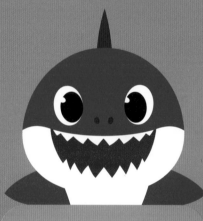

Daddy Shark is a strong and mighty hunter. He is much more than just Baby Shark's father though, the two of them play together like best friends!

BABY SHARK STORYBOOK SERIES

Baby Shark and the Colourful Balloons

Centum

Baby Turtle

Baby Turtle likes to play on the coral slide. When she is startled, she hides her head inside her turtle shell.

Baby Seahorse

Baby Seahorse always seems to run away when the mischievous Octopus Sisters are around.

Baby Whale

Baby Whale is very shy and often feels lonely. She likes to play on the see-saw.

Grandma Shark

Grandma Shark likes to read. She is a kind and thoughtful grandma who always has time to spend with Baby Shark.

Grandpa Shark

Grandpa Shark is wise and smart. He is famous for his hot clam buns and he loves to share his love of cooking with Baby Shark.

Baby Shark is looking
for his friends.
'Huh?! Where is everyone?'
wonders Baby Shark.

'I am so bored!' says Baby Shark.
To entertain himself, Baby Shark starts
to sing his favourite song.

'Baby Shark, doo-doo-doo-doo-doo!
Happy as a lark, doo-doo-doo-doo-doo!'

CREEEEAAAK!

Suddenly, a treasure chest opens with a loud creak.

A bunch of balloons float out of the chest.

'Colourful balloons!'
Baby Shark says in delight.

'Balloons are so much fun!'
shouts Baby Shark, as he happily swims this way
and that way with the balloons tied to his tail.

'ToooOO... ...fasssst!'

Hold on! Who is that on the coral slide?

It's Baby Turtle!

She likes to play on the coral slide.

'Oh dear! Are you okay, Baby Turtle?'

Baby Shark puts a plaster on the bump
on Baby Turtle's head, then he hands
Baby Turtle a yellow balloon.

Baby Turtle is smiling once again.
'It doesn't hurt anymore!' says Baby Turtle.
Baby Shark and Baby Turtle sing and giggle together
as they swim this way and that way
with their balloons.

'Yellow balloon,
doo-doo-doo-doo-doo!'

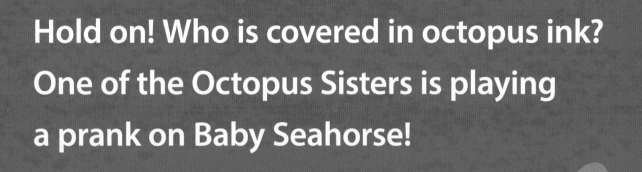

Hold on! Who is covered in octopus ink?
One of the Octopus Sisters is playing
a prank on Baby Seahorse!

'Oh dear, are you okay, Baby Seahorse?'
Baby Shark asks.
The friends work together to wash all of the ink
off Baby Seahorse, then Baby Shark gives him
a red balloon.

Baby Seahorse is smiling once again.

'I am not sad anymore!' says Baby Seahorse.

The friends swim together this way and that way with their balloons.

'Baby Seahorse, doo-doo-doo-doo!'

'Happy of course,
doo-doo-doo-doo-doo!'

Hold on! Who is sitting all alone on the see-saw?
Baby Whale is alone again and she feels left out.

'I am so lonely!'

'Oh dear! Are you okay, Baby Whale?'
ask Baby Shark. 'Don't feel blue, your
good friends are here with you!'

All the friends jump on the other end
of the see-saw and they hand Baby Whale
a green balloon.

All the friends are happy together and they are all smiling as they hold their balloons.
Best friends always have the best time together!

'Hey, everyone, doo-doo-doo-doo-doo!

"Singing is fun, doo-doo-doo-doo-doo!"